German Expressionist Watercolors

IN AMERICAN COLLECTIONS

September 18 - October 19, 1969

NATIONAL GALLERY OF ART
Washington, D.C.

Introduction

Among the purposes of a national gallery is to honor not only those who have created great works of art but those who have collected them; people born, in most cases, with that special gift, an "eye," and with the conviction to transform their love into possession.

Thus when the National Gallery of Art was given the privilege of exhibiting for the first time in America the extraordinary collection of German Expressionist watercolors from Cologne, it occurred to us that this would be a happy occasion to call attention to the quality of collecting in this field that has been going on in the United States. In supplementing the Wallraf-Richartz Museum's holdings, we have attempted to give a fuller representation to certain artists, particularly Klee and Kandinsky, and to include two artists, Marc and Beckmann, not in the Cologne group.

Controversial as much of this art has been, the twentieth century will take its place, I am convinced, with its predecessors as a powerful generator of lasting visual achievements. I believe this show, restricted though it is to the intimate and modestly-scaled medium of watercolor, bears out this conviction.

I wish to extend my personal thanks to the staff of the National Gallery in the preparation of this show, and particularly to Messrs William P. Campbell, Grose Evans, and E. John Bullard. Above all I would like to express my lasting appreciation to the American collectors who have so generously allowed us to take their treasures away from them for the duration of this exhibition.

J. Carter Brown
Director

Catalogue

The dimensions are given in inches, height preceding width.

Max Beckmann
1884-1950

1 STILL LIFE WITH FLOWERS
Watercolor, 20 x 25½ in. Date: 1933
Inscribed at lower left: Beckmann / 33
Lent by Morton D. May

2 BROTHER AND SISTER
Watercolor, 25¼ x 19½ in.
Inscribed at lower left: Beckmann / 37
Lent by Mrs. Mathilde Q. Beckmann

3 UNTITLED [Woman on man's lap]
Gouache, 24 x 18¾ in. Date: 1938
Inscribed at lower right: Beckmann / A 38
Lent by Mr. and Mrs. David Lloyd Kreeger

Lyonel Feininger
1871-1956

4 VOLLERSRODA
Watercolor and ink, 9½ x 12½ in.
Inscribed at bottom: Feininger Vollersroda
    Mittwoch d. 27. Sept. 1916
Lent anonymously

5 GABERNDORF
Watercolor and ink, 9⅜ x 12¼ in.
Inscribed at bottom: Feininger Gaberndorf
    Mittwoch d. 9. Jan. 1918
Lent anonymously

6 GASSE
Watercolor and ink, 15¾ x 12 in.
Inscribed at bottom: Feininger GASSE 10 APR.
    1923
Lent anonymously

Wassily Kandinsky
1866-1944

7 WHITE CLOUD
Watercolor and gouache, 16¼ x 14 in. Date: 1905
Lent by Mr. and Mrs. David Lloyd Kreeger

8 IMPROVISATION WITH RED SPOT
Watercolor, 19 x 25 in.
Inscribed at lower left: Kandinsky 1911
Lent by Mr. and Mrs. David Lloyd Kreeger

9 COW IN MOSCOW
Watercolor, 11 x 12¼ in. Date: c.1912
Inscribed at lower right: K [enclosed in triangle]
Lent anonymously

10 SKIZZE
Watercolor, 11⅝ x 13⅝ in. Date: 1912
Inscribed at lower right: K [enclosed in triangle]
Lent by Mr. and Mrs. Joseph H. Lauder

11 ABSTRACTION--RED CORNER
Gouache, 14¼ x 15¾ in. Date: 1914
Inscribed at lower left: K
Lent by Mr. and Mrs. Sidney Elliott Cohn

Paul Klee
1879-1940

12 HANNAH I
Wash, 7 x 4¼ in. Date: 1910
Inscribed at upper left: Klee; and on mount at
    bottom: Hannah I   66   1910
Lent by Frederick C. Schang, Sr.

13 TWO LADIES
Wash, 5 x 4 in. Date: 1911
Inscribed at upper left: Klee; and on mount at
    bottom: 2 Damen 1911 38
Lent by Frederick C. Schang, Sr.

14 VIEW OF THE SQUARE
Watercolor, 7 x 10⅝ in. Date: 1912
Inscribed at lower right: Klee; and on mount at
    bottom: Blick auf einem Platz 1912 10
Lent by Mr. and Mrs. Sidney Elliott Cohn

15 THE HOPELESS

Watercolor, 5 x 8½ in. Date: 1914
Inscribed at upper left: Klee; and on mount at
  lower left: 1914 58. Die Hoffnungslosen
Lent by Marian Willard Johnson

16 VIEW OF ST. GERMAIN

Watercolor, 9 x 11 in. Date: 1914
Inscribed at upper left: Klee; and on mount at
  lower right: 1914. 41. Ansicht v. St. Germain
Lent by Dr. and Mrs. Howard D. Sirak

17 PORTRAIT OF A DOLL

Wash, 10½ x 7½ in. Date: 1915
Inscribed at lower right: Klee; and on mount
  at lower left: 1915 237
Lent by Frederick C. Schang, Sr.

18 ON THE LAWN

Watercolor and ink, 8⅞ x 11⅞ in. Date: 1923
Inscribed at lower right: Klee
Lent by Mrs. Daniel R. Dunning

19 LITTLE WINTER LANDSCAPE WITH A GIRL
  BY A BROOK

Watercolor, 6¼ x 8¾ in. Date: 1924
Inscribed at lower left: Klee; and at lower right:
  24 4/12; and on mount at bottom: 1924.86.
    Kl. Winterlandschaft mit dem Madchen am Bach
Lent anonymously

August Macke
1887-1914

20 ST. GERMAIN BEI TUNIS

Watercolor and pencil, 11½ x 9 in. Date: 1914
Lent anonymously

Franz Marc
1880-1916

21 RESTING CALF

Watercolor, 15⅝ x 18⅛ in. Date: 1912
Lent anonymously

22 THE BULL

Watercolor, 15½ x 17¼ in. Date: 1913
Inscribed at lower left: M.
Lent by Mr. and Mrs. Robert S. Benjamin

23 TWO GAZELLES

Watercolor, 4 x 8¼ in. Date: 1913
Inscribed at lower right: F.M.
Lent by Mr. and Mrs. John D. Schiff

Max Pechstein
1881-1955

24 BATHERS

Watercolor and crayon, 19½ x 14⅞ in.
Inscribed at lower right: HMP [in monogram] 1920
National Gallery of Art, Rosenwald Collection

Karl Schmidt-Rottluff
1884-

25 AUTUMN LANDSCAPE

Watercolor, 19⅝ x 25½ in.
Inscribed at lower left: S Rottluff
National Gallery of Art, Rosenwald Collection

26 YELLOW IRIS

Watercolor, 27 x 19⅛ in.
Inscribed at lower left: S Rottluff
National Gallery of Art, Rosenwald Collection

Acknowledgments

Ever since the time of Dürer and the Masters of the Danube School there have always been German artists who have excelled in the medium of watercolor. Indeed, many have found their finest, most lasting expression in these spontaneous and fragile works on paper.

Again and again, these artists have selected the medium of watercolor to record both precise observations of nature and fleeting images of the imagination, of movement, light and shade. Among them, the Expressionists deserve particular attention, and we are fortunate to be able to present a selection of more than seventy of such masterpieces in this exhibition. All are lent by the Wallraf-Richartz Museum in Cologne from its justly famous Haubrich Collection. None has been shown in this country before and we are, therefore, very pleased to present them first at the National Gallery of Art, to be followed by exhibitions in several other museums.

The exhibition could not have come to life without the enthusiasm of the Director of the Wallraf-Richartz Museum, Dr. Horst Keller, who made the selection and wrote the Introduction to this catalogue. The Director General of the Cologne Museums, Professor Dr. Gert van der Osten, also contributed greatly to the preparation of the show, as did Dr. Hella Robels, who is responsible for the scholarly catalogue entries. Dr. Kurt Hackenberg, Chief of the Cultural Office of the City of Cologne, was instrumental in furthering the loan arrangements.

The German Government has for many years generously encouraged important traveling exhibitions. His Excellency, Rolf Pauls, The Ambassador of Germany, has kindly agreed to sponsor the exhibition of "German Expressionist Watercolors" during its tour, and we wish to express our deepest gratitude to him, and to the Cultural Attaché, Dr. J. Wilhelm von Buddenbrock, who has devoted considerable time and energy to this project. Dr. Karl Maes of the German Embassy also assisted us in every way with preparations for the opening at the National Gallery.

We also wish to thank Mrs. Leslie Judd Ahlander and Mr. Kurt Wiener for their assistance in the editing and preparation of this catalogue.

ANNEMARIE H. POPE
President
International Exhibitions Foundation

Introduction

WATERCOLORS OF THE GERMAN EXPRESSIONISTS

The first decade of the 19th century comprised the period of German Romantic painting. It was the time of Caspar David Friedrich, that great but lonely figure who is still not properly known to the wider world. A hundred years would pass before the artists of Germany would feel the call to create a new art from their personal experience, which was to transform artistic expression. This came about near the turn of the century through the art since known by the term "Expressionism."

"Every artist who, directly and without falsification, records his creative urge is one of us," wrote the painter, Ernst Ludwig Kirchner, in the printed program of the "Künstlergruppe Brücke" (The "Bridge" Group) in 1909. Emotion, truth, sincerity, capacity for experience, intensity of feeling, youthfulness — all these were demanded and promised by Kirchner, in the program. But what is the inner meaning of the German artists' venture into a new unknown realm? The painters no longer wished to work with the deceptive surface charm of the formal picture; they wanted to explore the "inward aspect" of landscape, its essential meaning. They sought the expressiveness of a face, a movement; they wanted a new reality in art. And while they believed in the deep, even psychological, impact of colors and form, boldly intensifying and changing them, they also sought powerful distortions which totally transformed the optical reality: in fact, plainly contradict it. Art had thus become one single exclamation of "jubilation," as well as of despair. This artistic cry, which Dürer himself had uttered centuries before, was recognized as the sole justification for art. This was to be the inner purpose and content of Expressionism.

In the atmosphere of that period, sixty years ago, it soon became evident that Ernst Ludwig Kirchner's call for unfalsified creation could not hope to find immediate sympathetic understanding. And so he searched for kindred souls, and began to build a bridge to the few sympathetic artists of the time. The group, which significantly called itself "Die Brücke" (The "Bridge"), was actually at first a voluntary association of four young artists, Heckel, Kirchner, Bleyl and Schmidt-Rottluff. They shared an empty store in Dresden as their studio. Soon Max Pechstein joined them. Emil Nolde came in later for a short time, and Otto Mueller embraced their ideas. The painters of the "Blaue Reiter" (Blue Rider Group): Kandinsky, Jawlensky, Klee, Franz Marc, August Macke, with his Swiss friend and colleague, Moilliet, Feininger and Kubin, followed similar paths.

An isolated figure, Christian Rohlfs, oldest of the group, changed his style as a painter in his later years, under the influence of this common "emotion." This feeling in turn influenced Kokoschka, who by the time he was twenty, had already achieved great power as an expressive painter of humanity.

Otto Dix and George Grosz, who were actually a second generation, were painters of big city life. Outraged by the social injustices of their time, they scourged the bigotry and decadence of their world with their angry art. They saw that world as plunging into an abyss — a view that history has born out. These are a few of the artists most intimately connected with the German Expressionist movement in art.

Of these artists, only Otto Dix, Erich Heckel, Oskar Kokoschka and Karl Schmidt-Rottluff are still living, advanced in age but united by idea and creativity.

Everything that happened at this time in art was of surprising violence, both in painting and in the graphic arts, which had been newly rediscovered. But watercolors and colored drawings were just as brilliant, indeed, often uniquely fresh and lovely. It was a rare phenomenon not confined to German art, that over and above oil painting, with its solid and often strong colors, and the earlier powerful drypoints and color prints, the transparent, delicate watercolor should re-enter the artistic scene at the beginning of our century. It is of equal quality, often at the highest level of achievement, and saturated with the Expressionist vision.

This exhibition of watercolors, from the collections of the Wallraf-Richartz Museum, is surely a convincing demonstration of this thesis. It is a pure joy to the eye to see these pictures, now historic but still so glowingly fresh, looking as though they were created yesterday. Their language is astounding even today, when more than a generation has drawn strength from their new, fresh vision. The language of the watercolor has its own veracity, for while the paint on these pictures is very thin, they derive their very brilliance from this transparent, magical color, tenuous as a breath. Truly, a "jubilation of color" is visible here, with all its transparence and deliberate contrast between paint and adjacent paper, a contrast which watercolor had not hitherto known. (The art, after all, goes back to the time of Dürer, who also made watercolors of the explosive moods of nature.) But at the beginning of this century, only the contemporary "Fauves" in Paris, while more controlled, achieved similar results. They did not, however, ascribe as much importance to watercolor as did the German Expressionists.

The watercolors and drawings in color presented in this exhibition were done mainly in the years between 1905 and 1925. They present works of artists whose pictures can be seen in various museums in the United States, though in limited numbers. More important have been individual events like the great exhibition of Ernst Ludwig Kirchner. But by its nature, watercolor cannot become well known, because it is exhibited for only limited periods, so as to protect it from fading. The pictures gathered here from the graphic collections of the Wallraf-Richartz Museum in Cologne have the charm of rediscovery even for Cologne art lovers, when the watercolors are brought out of their boxes from time to time.

What can be chosen as the common denominator in such an exhibit? It is actually a gathering of the work of great individualists, whether they belong to a group or expressly shun any "direction." All these artists loved watercolor, except perhaps Kubin, a draftsman, and George Grosz, for whom color had an interpretive character. They were all painters and

6

wood carvers, sculptors and designers of tapestries — that is, artists in the finest and most comprehensive sense of the word. Thus they were not primarily watercolorists: they simply loved the art of watercolor.

The various techniques of this creative group may be indicated in a few brief remarks. Perhaps it will serve to clarify the directions opened by an art which aimed at "the renewal of existence." In fact, it not only renewed creation; it transformed it. From the contemporary point of view, it seems as though their art were a pictorial prophesy, well before the great social reforms came about.

With the survey of master watercolors offered by this exhibition, an outline of the movement can be summed up, more as differentiation than as common denominator. But the very differences between the artists serve as witness to the strength of the individual, who often suffered for his independence. Briefly: ERNST LUDWIG KIRCHNER, the innovator and pioneer among these painters, was fascinated by human beings, seeing them with a dry brittle vision, in a kind of spiritual interpretation. But Kirchner was later equally drawn to the urban scene. Still later he moved to the solitude of the Swiss Alps where he composed pastoral idylls in a primitive, tart pictorial language, followed by a thorny and barbed style. ERICH HECKEL, compared to Kirchner and the other artists of the "Brücke," was stylistically less aggressive in his description of man and nature. In his work he revealed the emotions of a crypto-Gothic personality, and his human models often approached this desired form.

In decided contrast to Heckel is KARL SCHMIDT-ROTTLUFF. His paintings, like his woodcuts, are constantly preoccupied with primitive art, which affected him powerfully. And so it was almost inevitable that he should paint in simplified, blocklike forms, in which he combined exotic cult scenes with plant elements. In his later, often more ingratiating still lifes, this impression of a deliberately rather barbaric style was not diluted.

MAX PECHSTEIN, for all his obvious inclination toward pretty coloring, followed Schmidt-Rottluff's path, at least in the "classic" years of Expressionism just before the First World War.

EMIL NOLDE will always be the inspired individualist in this art form. He obtained more original effects from watercolor than anyone before him; he is perhaps the greatest of all modern watercolorists. An absorbent surface like Japanese paper which, when moistened, is like blotting paper, was the right, and indeed almost the only suitable surface for his technique. His subjects are the product of a vision of the world in which the active forces of nature seem to be transformed into fabulous imagery, with half-beings melting into a dream cosmos of glowing color. Nolde recorded his constant amazement at the world, at his homeland and his recollections of the Far East. He rendered them in the same burning luminous colors that he used for his emotional and religious investigations and experiences.

As with Paul Klee, his watercolors stand as complete works of art, demanding no further transformation, and especially not into oils.

OTTO MUELLER devoted his early art to those nomadic, cheerful children of nature, the gypsies. Later he again found, in his nude girl bathers among the reeds, a lost Arcadia, a province of carefree existence.

The term "Expressionism" has also been applied to artists who made no secret of their individualism, who indeed resisted absorption and activity in a group. They include the ever masterful OSKAR KOKOSCHKA, who was born in Austria, but has worked all over the world. He is a watercolorist of brilliant resolution. Finally CHRISTIAN ROHLFS was of this company of individualists. He was a painter who, on the threshold of old age, radically altered his style and invented delicate, floating motifs, which dissolved into an ecstasy of color. The subjects were mostly of farms and small-town houses and gardens, a homage to the place of his birth, Soest. To catalogue Paul Klee's subtle works in watercolor would require an analysis of style which is impossible in relation to the few pictures on view. Nevertheless his watercolors exhibited in the show indicate how closely the draftsman and the painter are wed in every picture.

Among these artists, GEORGE GROSZ and OTTO DIX were the interpreters and protesters against contemporary social conditions. With scorching precision and a brilliant gift for exposing human weakness, they come close to the border between painting and caricature. The irony of their attitude toward human existence is not to be missed. Each in his separate way used color as an emotional resource, a painterly ingredient interpreting the role of drawing. For their art is not an end in itself. Arising as it did under the pressure of the horrors of the First World War it aims to shock.

Lastly there remains ALFRED KUBIN, an individualist who seems to carry on a permanent dialogue with the spirits which terrify him. As a draftsman he remains alone. His visions, which alternate between a world of fantasy and one of reality, are informally drawn. They are usually enriched with a little color, and at times seem similar to the early Klee, though not following him on his "inward path." Kubin remains fascinated by visions coming from the outer world.

These remarks are not intended as references to particular pictures. They aim only at describing what impresses the eye. Both masters and pictures are witnesses to an epoch of German art whose achievement was, among other things, to have brought the creativity of art in Germany back into prominence outside its frontiers, after a lapse of centuries. This exhibition will, within its own scope, underline that achievement.

HORST KELLER

Catalogue

All works shown are illustrated under their catalogue numbers.

The dimensions are given in inches and centimeters, height preceding width.

Otto Dix

Born 1891 near Gera. Moved to Dresden 1909—14 where he attended the School of Arts and Crafts. Again in Dresden 1919—22, then to Düsseldorf, 1922—25; studied at the Academy there and was a member of "Das Junge Rheinland" group. In Berlin 1925—27. In Dresden 1927—33 as Professor at the Academy of Arts. Dismissed by Hitler regime in 1933, he settled in Randegg near Singen. Since 1936 lived in Hemmenhofen near Radolfzell on Lake Constance. Died 1969 in Hemmenhofen.

1 STREET SCENE
Watercolor with pen and ink on cardboard.
19⁵/₈ x 15³/₄ in. (49.3 x 39.7 cm.)
Signed and dated at l. l.: Dix 22
Haubrich Collection, 1946

2 THE WINDOW
Watercolor with pencil on cardboard.
15³/₄ x 12 in. (39.7 x 30.0 cm.)
Signed and dated at l. r.: Dix 23/202; inscribed on reverse: Das Fenster
Haubrich Collection, 1946

3 PORTRAIT OF FRAU DR. KOCH
Watercolor over pencil and pen on paper.
24¹/₄ x 19¹/₄ in. (60.6 x 48.2 cm.)
Signed and dated at l. l.: Dix 23/227; inscribed on reverse: Für Karl Nierendorf
Haubrich Collection, 1946

Lyonel Feininger

Born 1871 in New York, died there 1956. The son of immigrant German musicians; 1887—88 attended School of Arts and Crafts in Hamburg, then Berlin Academy, then 1892—93 Académie Colarossi, Paris.

Worked as a cartoonist in Berlin until 1906. In Paris 1906—08, where he became acquainted with Cubism, followed by travel. Exhibited in the first German Autumn Salon, Berlin 1913 with the "Blaue Reiter" group. Appointed to the Bauhaus in Weimar in 1919, rejoined Kandinsky, Klee and Jawlensky to form the "Blauen Vier" group and exhibited with them. Left Bauhaus when it moved to Dessau, but retained contact until 1933. Maintained a studio in Halle; lived in Berlin 1933—36 when he returned to the U. S.

4 HEILIGENHAFEN
Watercolor with pen and ink on brown tinted paper. 11³/₄ x 15¹/₈ in. (29.6 x 37.8 cm.)
Signed, inscribed and dated at bottom: Feininger HEILIGENHAFEN Mont. d. 20. Feb. 1922
Haubrich Collection, 1946

5 KLEIN-SCHWABHAUSEN
Watercolor with pen and ink on paper.
10¹/₂ x 14 in. (26.2 x 35.2 cm.)
Signed, inscribed, and dated at bottom: Feininger Kl. Schwabhausen Sonnabend d. 26. Januar 1924
Haubrich Collection, 1946

George Grosz

Born 1893 in Berlin, died there 1959. 1909, studied at Academy of Art, Dresden; 1912, School of Arts and Crafts, Berlin. 1918, co-founder of the Berlin Dada movement. 1922—25, travel to Russia, Scandinavia, Paris; 1932, visiting instructor, Art Students League, New York; immigration to U. S. 1933. Occasional faculty member, Art Students League 1933—51; 1941—42, taught at Art Department, Columbia University. Visits to Berlin 1954, 1958; returned to live in Berlin in 1959.

6 VIGOR AND GRACE
Watercolor with pen and ink on paper.
21¹/₄ x 17¹/₂ in. (53.3 x 44 cm.)
c. 1922
Signed at l. r.: GROSZ; inscribed on reverse: Frau, Strumpfband befestigend
Haubrich Collection, 1946

7 LITTLE CAFÉ
Watercolor with pen and brown ink on paper.
24³/₈ x 19¹/₈ in. (60.9 x 47.9 cm.)
c. 1922/24
Signed at l. r.: GROSZ
Haubrich Collection, 1946

8 MASKED BALL
Watercolor with pen and brown ink on paper.
20⁷/₈ x 26 in. (52.2 x 64.8 cm.)
c. 1925
Signed at l. r.: GROSZ; inscribed on the reverse:
Gesellschaft, Rohrfeder
Haubrich Collection, 1946

Erich Heckel

Born 1883 in Döbeln, Saxony. 1901, met Schmidt-
Rottluff in Chemnitz; 1905, studied architecture at
Technical College, Dresden, where he met Kirchner
and Bleyl and became co-founder of the "Brücke"
group. 1909, travel to Italy; settled in Berlin 1911.
1919–44, extensive travel to France, England,
Austria, Baltic states, Switzerland and Italy. 1944
settled in Hemmenhofen, Lake Constance where
he now lives.

9 SEATED WOMAN
Watercolor, pencil and gouache on Japanese
paper. 23 x 17³/₄ in. (57.6 x 44.2 cm.)
Signed, dated and titled at l. r.: Erich Heckel 19
Sitzende
Haubrich Collection, 1946

10 LANDSCAPE
Watercolor and gouache over charcoal on paper.
17¹/₄ x 23¹/₄ in. (43.4 x 58.2 cm.)
Signed and dated at l. r.: Erich Heckel 19;
Titled at l. l.: Landschaft.
Haubrich Collection, 1946

11 HEAD OF A MAN
Watercolor and gouache over black chalk on
paper. 24¹/₂ x 18⁵/₈ in. (61.2 x 46.8 cm.)
Signed, dated and titled at l. l.: Erich Heckel
23 Männerkopf
Haubrich Collection, 1946

12 MOUNTAINOUS LANDSCAPE NEAR
OBERSTDORF (ALLGÄU)
Watercolor and gouache over black chalk on
paper. 20¹/₂ x 24¹/₂ in. (51.2 x 61.5 cm.)
Signed, dated and titled at l. r.: Gebirgstal
Erich Heckel 23
Haubrich Collection, 1946

Alexei von Jawlensky

Born 1864 in Torshok, Russia, died 1941 in Wiesbaden. 1889, attended St. Petersburg Academy;
1890, studied with Ilja Repin; 1891 met and worked
with Marianne von Werefkin. 1896, moved to
Munich; acquaintance with Kandinsky. 1907 in
Paris, visit to Matisse's studio. 1909, founding
member of "Neue Künstlervereinigung München."
1917, moved to Switzerland and to Wiesbaden in
1922. Joined Klee, Kandinsky and Feininger in
1924 to form the "Blauen Vier" group.

13 HEAD
Watercolor and ink on paper.
7¹/₂ x 6 in. (18.8 x 15.3 cm.)
c. 1921
Signed at l. l.: A. J.
Wilhelm Strecker Collection, Wiesbaden, 1958

Wassily Kandinsky

Born 1866 in Moscow, died Neuilly-sur-Seine,
France, 1944. Studied Law and Economics in
Moscow and Odessa. Began study of painting in
Munich 1896 at Asbé School under Stuck. 1901,
opened his "Phalanx" association of artists;
member of the Berlin Secession; the German
Federation of Artists and the Paris Autumn Salon.
1903–07, travel to Tunisia, Holland, Italy; Paris,
Berlin and Dresden. In 1909 he founded the "Neue
Künstlervereinigung München," collaborated with
Marc, Macke, and Klee. 1911–13, he produced
the almanac "Der Blaue Reiter" with Marc and
later formed a new group with the same name by
Marc, Klee, Campendonk, Kubin, Macke, Werefkin,

Münter and others. At outbreak of World War I he returned to Russia and after the revolution there assumed various official positions, including that of Professor of Art Theory. 1921, return to Germany; 1922–33 Professor at Bauhaus in Weimar and Dessau; thereafter moved to France.

14 RIDERS ON THE BEACH
Watercolor on paper. 12$^1/_2$ x 19$^1/_8$ in.
(31.5 x 48.0 cm.)
c. 1911
Signed at l. l.: K
Haubrich Collection, 1951

Ernst Ludwig Kirchner

Born 1880 in Aschaffenburg, died 1938 in Wildboden/Frauenkirch near Davos. 1901–05, studied architecture at the Dresden Technical College; 1905 founded the "Brücke" group with Heckel, Bleyl and Schmidt-Rottluff. 1911, moved to Berlin; military training in Halle in World War I. Mental and physical breakdown compelled a stay in a sanatorium. 1917, he moved to Switzerland. Repeated journeys to Germany. Ill and distraught over the Hitler regime and artistic defamation he committed suicide.

15 THE MODEL
Watercolor with pencil on cardboard.
11$^1/_8$ x 14$^7/_8$ in. (27.8 x 37.2 cm.)
c. 1908
Signed at l. l.: Kirchner. On reverse: Landscape with Pond, watercolor; signed at l. l.: E. L. Kirchner and dated in pencil: 02

16 LANDSCAPE NEAR MORITZBURG
Watercolor with ink and pencil on paper.
14$^5/_8$ x 18$^3/_8$ in. (36.8 x 46.0 cm.)
c. 1909
Signed and wrongly dated at l. r.: EL Kirchner 06
Presented by the Wilhelm Grosshennig Gallery, Düsseldorf, 1953

17 STEAMER ON THE ELBE
Watercolor with pencil on paper.
9$^1/_8$ x 13$^3/_4$ in. (23.0 x 34.4 cm.)
c. 1910
Wrongly dated at l. r.: 04; signed on reverse:
E. L. Kirchner 04 and stamped with estate mark
(A Dre/Ab4)
Presented by Herr Albert Daberkow, Bad Homburg, 1956

18 SLEEPING
Pencil and colored oil crayon on paper.
10$^3/_4$ x 13$^1/_2$ in. (27.1 x 34.0 cm.)
c. 1911/12
Signed on reverse: E. L. Kirchner
Haubrich Collection, 1946

19 PORTRAIT OF A MAN
Gouache and pencil on cardboard.
17 x 12$^3/_8$ in. (42.6 x 31.0 cm.)
c. 1914
On reverse: Pencil sketch for same portrait and estate mark: A/Ba 14 (K 3910)
Acquired, 1962

20 NUDE AT THE STOVE
Watercolor with pencil and black chalk on paper.
20 x 15$^1/_8$ in. (50.0 x 38.0 cm.)
c. 1914
Signed at l. ctr.: Herrn Prof. Könen E. L. Kirchner
Haubrich Collection, 1952

21 PEASANTS IN A PASTURE
Watercolor and charcoal on paper.
12$^3/_4$ x 14$^3/_4$ in. (32.1 x 37.1 cm.)
Signed and dated l. l.: EL Kirchner 19; on reverse:
View of Frankfort, pen and ink Estate Mark:
A Da/bc5
Presented by Bayer Co., Leverkusen, commemorating its Centenary, 1963

22 HERDSMAN AND CALVES
Watercolor and pencil on cardboard.
20 x 14$^1/_2$ in. (50.0 x 36.5 cm.)
c. 1920
Signed at l. r.: K; below: E. L. Kirchner (in a different hand)
Haubrich Collection, 1946

1924 291.   Klang aus Sicilien

23 FIR TREES
Watercolor with pencil on paper.
24¹/₂ x 17 in. (61.5 x 42.5 cm.)
c. 1920
Signed at l. r.: K
Haubrich Collection, 1946

24 SWISS PEASANTS
Watercolor with gouache and pencil on paper.
20 x 15¹/₈ in. (50.0 x 38.0 cm.)
Signed at u. l.: E L Kirchner; titled and dated on
reverse: Zwei Bauernköpfe 1921
Haubrich Collection, 1946

25 YOUNG MAN AND GARDENHOUSE
Watercolor and gouache on paper.
19³/₈ x 14¹/₂ in. (48.5 x 36.5 cm.)
Signed at l. r.: E L Kirchner; titled and dated on
reverse: Junger Mann v. der Laube 1923
Haubrich Collection, 1946

Paul Klee

Born 1879 in Munchenbuchsee/Berne, died 1940
in Muralto/Locarno. The son of a German musi-
cian, he studied in Munich under Knirr in 1898,
later at the Academy under Stuck. 1901, travel to
Italy; 1905 in Paris, moved to Munich in 1906. Met
Kubin, Kandinsky, Marc and Macke; in 1911/12
joined the "Blaue Reiter" group. 1912 in Paris;
1914 travel to Tunisia with Macke and Moilliet.
From 1921 at the Bauhaus in Weimar and Dessau;
1924 founder member of the "Blauen Vier" in
Weimar. 1931 until dismissed in 1933, Professor at
Düsseldorf Academy. Spent his last years in
Switzerland.

26 DUNE PICTURE
Watercolor with pen and ink on paper.
8⁷/₈ x 9 in. (22.4 x 22.7 cm.)
Signed at l. r.: Klee. Dated and titled further down
on r.: 24 5/12 1924 177 Dünenbild
Acquired 1958 with Wilhelm Strecker Collection,
Wiesbaden

27 MELODY FROM SICILY
Watercolor on paper. 6⁷/₈ x 8⁷/₈ in. (17.2 x 22.2 cm.)
Signed at u. r.: Klee. Dated and titled below:
1924.291 Klang aus Sizilien
Acquired, 1958 with Wilhelm Strecker Collection,
Wiesbaden

Oskar Kokoschka

Born 1886 in Pöchlarn, Austria. 1905—09 Vienna
School of Arts and Crafts. Active in Wiener Werk-
stätte 1907—09. Travel to Switzerland and Berlin
where he became acquainted with the "Sturm"; to
Italy in 1913. World War I volunteer, severely
wounded in 1915; return to Vienna; war cor-
respondent on front. 1917—24 in Dresden, taught
at the academy there 1919. Extensive travel
1923—33; lived in Prague 1934—38; in London
1938—52. Since 1953 he lives in Villeneuve,
Switzerland with intermittent travel to England,
Austria, Germany, Italy, the United States, Den-
mark and Greece.

28 STANDING GIRL
Watercolor on paper. 27⁷/₈ x 20³/₄ in. (69.9 x 51.8 cm.)
c. 1922/23
Signed at l. r.: O Kokoschka
Haubrich Collection, 1946

29 PORTRAIT OF A GIRL
Watercolor on paper. 27³/₈ x 20³/₄ in. (68.6 x 52.0 cm.)
c. 1922/23
Signed at l. l.: O Kokoschka
Haubrich Collection, 1946

30 PORTRAIT OF DR. VICTOR WALLERSTEIN
Watercolor on paper. 28³/₈ x 20³/₄ in. (70.7 x 52.0 cm.)
c. 1922/23
Signed at l. r.: O Kokoschka
Haubrich Collection, 1954

31 FIGURE OF A GIRL
Watercolor on paper. 20¹/₂ x 27¹/₈ in. (51.3 x 68.1 cm.)
c. 1922/23
Signed at l. r.: O Kokoschka
Haubrich Collection, 1946

Alfred Kubin

Born 1877 in Leitmeritz, Bohemia, died 1959 in Wernstein, Austria. Attended Salzburg School of Arts and Crafts; 1892—96 worked in photography atelier of Beer in Klagenfurt. 1898—1901 studied in Munich and had first exhibition in 1902 at Bruno Cassirer in Berlin. 1909, joined "Neue Künstler-vereinigung München" and became a member of the "Blaue Reiter" group in 1912. Was active mainly as illustrator.

32 CHAMOIS HUNTING
Watercolor with pen and ink on reverse of a survey map. 15⁵/₈ x 12¹/₂ in. (39.4 x 31.3 cm.)
c. 1912/15
Signed twice at l. r.: Kubin; titled at l. l.
Haubrich Collection, 1946

33 YOUNG STALLION WITH SNAKE (3rd version)
Watercolor with pen and ink on reverse of a survey map. 14⁵/₈ x 8⁷/₈ in. (36.8 x 29.8 cm.)
c. 1924
Signed at l. r.: A Kubin; titled at l. l.
Haubrich Collection, 1946

34 ILL-FAMED PLACE (2nd version)
Watercolor with pen and ink on reverse of a survey map. 12³/₈ x 15 in. (31.0 x 37.7 cm.)
Signed and dated at l. r.: Kubin 25 titled at l. l.
Acquired, 1930

August Macke

Born 1887 in Meschede, died 1914 Perthes-les-Hurlus, France. 1904—06 studied at Academy of Art and School of Arts and Crafts, Düsseldorf. 1905 first visit to Italy, followed by trips, 1906 to Holland, Belgium and London; 1907 to Paris. Winter 1907/8 he studied in Berlin with Lovis Corinth. 1908 second visit to Italy, to Paris 1908 and 1909. Met Franz Marc who introduced him to the "Neue Künstlervereinigung München" and began friendship with Kandinsky and Jawlensky. 1911/12 on the editorial committee for "Der Blaue Reiter" almanac and participated in exhibitions of the same title. In 1912 in Paris he met Delaunay and visited Tunisia with Klee and Moilliet in April, 1914. He was killed in action September 16, 1914.

35 THE HORSEBACK RIDE
Watercolor and gouache on paper.
9⁷/₈ x 13³/₈ in. (24.7 x 33.6 cm.)
Date: 1913 at l. r.: inscribed on reverse: 2 Reiter [in the hand of Frau Erdmann-Macke]
Macke, Aug. Spazierritt, estate mark No. 70
Purchased, 1922; confiscated, 1937, re-acquired from the art market 1952

36 DRESSMAKER'S WINDOW
Watercolor and gouache over pencil on paper.
11¹/₂ x 9 in. (29.0 x 22.7 cm.)
Signed and dated at l. r.: A Macke 13
A variant in oil is in the possession of Erik Blumenfeld, Hamburg
Acquired, 1933

37 ON THE LANDING BRIDGE IN THUN
Watercolor on paper. 7 x 5 in. (17.6 x 12.6 cm.)
Inscribed on reverse: August Macke 1914 Ländte in Thun [certified by Frau Erdmann-Macke]
Haubrich Collection, 1946

38 VILLAGE STREET
Watercolor over pencil on paper mounted on cardboard. 9¹/₂ x 12¹/₈ in. (20.4 x 30.2 cm.)
Inscribed on reverse: August Macke Aquarelle aus Kandern im Schwarzwald Juni 1914 Dorfstrasse [in the hand of Frau Erdmann-Macke]. In the possession of Stehling, Godesberg; estate mark No. 139
Haubrich Collection, 1948

Louis Moilliet

Born 1880 in Berne, died 1962 in La Tour-de-Peilz; 1900—03 studied in Worpswede, also Switzerland, Weimar; 1904 Stuttgart Academy of Art. In 1905 he went to Paris with Klee and Bloesch; 1907—09 travel to Italy, France and Tunisia. In 1910 he settled at Gunten where Macke visited him in 1911. Met Kandinsky and Marc in Munich, went to Tunisia with Macke and Klee in 1914.

39 KAIROUAN

Watercolor on paper. 9 x 11¼ in. (22.6 x 28.3 cm.)
Signed below r. of center: L Moilliet; further to l.:
Kairouan 1914
Acquired, 1953

Otto Mueller

Born 1874 in Liebau, Silesia, died 1930 in Breslau;
1890—94 studied lithography in Görlitz; 1894—96
at the Academy of Art in Dresden. Lived in Munich
1898—1908 with visits in Dresden 1899 and
Silesia where he moved in the circle of Carl and
Gerhart Hauptmann. In 1908 he settled in Berlin,
traveled to Bohemia with Kirchner. 1910 joined
the "Brücke" group. Friendship with Heckel.
Professor at Breslau Academy from 1919 until
his death.

40 SEATED NUDE

Watercolor with black and colored chalk on paper.
27¼ x 20¾ in. (68.2 x 52.0 cm.)
Signed at l. r.: Otto Mueller; on reverse: Girl's
Head (in brown chalk)
Acquired, 1924

41 GYPSIES IN FRONT OF THEIR TENT

Pen and ink, and wash with black and colored
chalk on paper. 23¾ x 18¾ in. (59.5 x 46.5 cm.)
Signed at l. l.: Otto Mueller
Haubrich Collection, 1946

42 PORTRAIT OF THE ARTIST'S WIFE

Watercolor with black and colored chalk on
blotting paper. 22½ x 18⅛ in. (56.4 x 45.4 cm.)
Signed at l. r.: Otto Mueller
Haubrich Collection, 1946

43 THREE NUDES

Colored oil crayon over light watercolor tinting on
paper. 27⅛ x 20 in. (68.0 x 50.0 cm.)
c. 1925
Signed at l. l.: Otto Mueller
Haubrich Collection, 1946

Emil Nolde (E. Hansen)

Born 1867 in Nolde, died 1956 in Seebüll. 1884—88
studied at Sauermann School of Carving in Flens-
burg; also in Munich and Karlsruhe. Moved to
Berlin 1899; taught at St. Gallen School of Arts
and Crafts 1892—98; followed by study in Munich,
Paris and Copenhagen. Joined the "Brücke"
group. Stays in Dresden, Hamburg, Copenhagen;
1913—14 travel to the South Sea Islands. 1921
travel to England, France and Spain.

44 CABARET SINGER

Watercolor with brush and ink on Japanese paper.
12³/₈ x 15 in. (31.0 x 37.5 cm.)
c. 1911
Signed at l. r.: Nolde
Acquired, 1923

45 CHINESE JUNKS

Watercolor with brush and ink on Japanese paper.
9⁵/₈ x 11 in. (24.2 x 27.8 cm.)
c. 1913
Signed at l. l.: Nolde
Haubrich Collection, 1946

46 JUNK

Watercolor with brush and ink on Japanese paper.
9½ x 13⅛ in. (23.9 x 33.0 cm.)
c. 1913
Signed at l. r.: Nolde
Acquired, 1925

47 JUNKS

Watercolor with brush and ink on Japanese paper.
7³/₄ x 10⁵/₈ in. (19.6 x 26.8 cm.)
c. 1913
Signed at l. l.: Nolde
Acquired, 1922

48 HEAD OF A SOUTH SEA ISLANDER

Watercolor and gouache with brush and ink on
brown-tinted Japanese paper.
19¼ x 14¼ in. (48.2 x 35.9 cm.)
c. 1914
Signed at l. l.: Nolde
Haubrich Collection, 1946

49 HEAD OF A SOUTH SEA ISLANDER IN
       MOURNING
Watercolor and gouache with brush and ink on
brown-tinted paper. 19³/₈ x 14¹/₄ in. (48.7 x 35.8 cm.)
c. 1914
Signed at l. r.: Nolde
Haubrich Collection, 1946

50 JOCHEN
Watercolor with brush and ink on Japanese paper.
18³/₄ x 13³/₄ in. (47.0 x 34.5 cm.)
c. 1916/18
Signed at l. l.: Nolde

51 EVENING CLOUDS
Watercolor with brush and ink on Japanese paper.
13 x 19³/₈ in. (32.7 x 48.5 cm.)
c. 1916/24
Signed at u. r.: Nolde
Acquired, 1924

52 NORTH SEA COAST
Watercolor with brush and ink on Japanese paper.
14 x 18³/₄ in. (35.0 x 47 .0 cm.)
c. 1916/26
Signed at l. r.: Nolde
Haubrich Collection, 1946

53 HEAD OF A SPANISH GIRL
Watercolor with brush and ink on yellow tinted
paper. 16¹/₄ x 12³/₄ in. (40.5 x 33.0 cm.)
c. 1921
Signed at l. r.: Nolde
Haubrich Collection, 1946

54 DANCER (MARY WIGMAN)
Watercolor on Japanese paper.
19¹/₈ x 14¹/₄ in. (47.7 x 35.2 cm.)
c. 1923
Signed at l. l.: Nolde
Acquired, 1958 with the Wilhelm Strecker
Collection, Wiesbaden
(cover illustration)

55 VAIL TAILS
Watercolor on Japanese paper.
14³/₈ x 16³/₄ in. (36.1 x 47.0 cm.)
Signed at l. r.: Nolde
Acquired, 1927

56 SUNSET AT LOW TIDE
Watercolor on Japanese paper.
14 x 19¹/₄ in. (35.0 x 48.2 cm.)
Signed at l. r.: Nolde
Haubrich Collection, 1946

57 COASTAL LANDSCAPE WITH MILL
Watercolor with brush and ink on Japanese paper.
14 x 18⁵/₈ in. (35.2 x 46.9 cm.)
Signed at l. r.: Nolde

58 THUNDERSHOWER OVER THE ESTUARY
Watercolor on Japanese paper.
13⁷/₈ x 19 in. (34.8 x 47.8 cm.)
Signed at l. r.: Nolde
Haubrich Collection, 1946

59 LIGHT-PLAY IN THE LAKE OF ZURICH
Watercolor on Japanese paper.
13⁷/₈ x 18³/₄ in. (34.8 x 46.8 cm.)
Signed at l. r.: Nolde
Haubrich Collection, 1946

60 MAN WITH HELMET
Watercolor with chalk and ink on paper.
12¹/₄ x 14 in. (30.5 x 35.0 cm.)
Signed at l. r.: Nolde
Acquired 1958 with the Wilhelm Strecker
Collection, Wiesbaden

Max Pechstein

Born 1881 in Zwickau, died 1955 Berlin. 1900—02
attended School of Arts and Crafts, 1902—06
Academy, Dresden. Joined the "Brücke" group in
1906 in Dresden. 1907 visits to Italy and Paris;
settled in Berlin 1908. Founder member of "Neue
Sezession" 1910; 1914 travel the South Seas and
lived on Palau Islands. 1915—18 soldier in the
army, partly on western front; returned to Berlin.
Exhibition of his work forbidden in 1934. From
1945 Professor at Hochschule für Bildende
Künste, Berlin.

61 FISHERMEN IN THE SURF
Watercolor with pencil on grey cardboard.
20¹/₂ x 29³/₄ in. (51.2 x 74.6 cm.)
Signed and dated at l. r.: H M Pechstein 1920
Haubrich Collection, 1946

Christian Rohlfs

Born 1849 in Niendorf, Holstein, died 1938 in Hagen. Attended Academy of Art, Weimar 1870; had his own studio from 1881. In 1897 first saw French Impressionist paintings and met Edvard Munch in 1898. In 1900 through Henry van de Velde he met Karl-Ernst Osthaus who appointed him to the Folkwang Museum then being built in Hagen. Expelled from Prussian Academy of Arts in 1937.

62 CHRYSANTHEMUMS
Watercolor, gouache and ink on paper.
22⁵/₈ x 15³/₈ in. (56.7 x 38.5 cm.)
Signed and dated at l. r.: CR 19
Haubrich Collection, 1946

63 PHILODENDRON
Watercolor and gouache on paper.
27¹/₄ x 20¹/₈ in. (68.3 x 50.2 cm.)
Signed and dated at l. r.: CR 20
Karl Bau Bequest, 1945

64 VASE WITH FLOWERS
Watercolor, gouache, brush and ink on paper.
28 x 20⁵/₈ in. (70.0 x 51.6 cm.)
Signed and dated at l. r.: CR 23
Haubrich Collection, 1946

65 STILL LIFE WITH VASE OF FLOWERS
Watercolor and gouache on paper.
19⁷/₈ x 27¹/₄ in. (49.8 x 68.3 cm.)
Signed and dated at l. r.: CR 26
Haubrich Collection, 1946

66 LANDSCAPE WITH DARK TREES
Watercolor and gouache on paper.
20³/₈ x 27¹/₄ in. (51.0 x 68.4 cm.)
Signed and dated at l. r.: CR 27
Haubrich Collection, 1946

Karl Schmidt-Rottluff

Born 1884 Rottluff. 1905, moved to Dresden to study architecture; founder member of the "Brücke" group. In contact with Heckel and Pech-

stein; 1911 settled in Berlin. 1930 a guest student at the Villa Massimo in Rome; 1933 expelled from Prussian Academy of Art. 1947 appointed Professor at Hochschule für Bildende Künste, Berlin.

67 KNEELING NUDE WITH RED KERCHIEF
Brush drawing with watercolor on paper.
18⁵/₈ x 23¹/₈ in. (46.7 x 58.0 cm.)
Signed and dated at l. r.: S. Rottluff 1913
Haubrich Collection, 1946

68 LUPINS IN A ROOM
Watercolor with pen and ink on paper.
19¹/₂ x 15³/₄ in. (49.0 x 39.5 cm.)
Signed and dated at l. l.: S. Rottluff 21; titled on reverse: Lupinen im Zimmer
Haubrich Collection, 1946

69 LILACS
Watercolor with pen and ink on paper.
19¹/₈ x 24³/₈ in. (48.0 x 61.0 cm.)
Signed and dated at l. r.: S. Rottluff 1922
Haubrich Collection, 1946

70 RIVER LANDSCAPE
Watercolor with pen and ink on paper.
19¹/₈ x 24³/₈ in. (48.0 x 61.0 cm.)
Signed and dated at l. r.: S. Rottluff 1922
Haubrich Collection, 1946

71 CASTLE IN THE TICINO
Watercolor on paper. 19³/₄ x 27¹/₄ in. (49.5 x 68.2 cm.)
c. 1928/29
Signed at l. l.: S. Rottluff
Haubrich Collection, 1946

72 EXOTIC STILL LIFE WITH BANANAS
Watercolor on paper. 27³/₄ x 20¹/₈ in. (69.5 x 50.2 cm.)
c. 1934
Signed at l. r.: S. Rottluff
Acquired, 1947

A selection of the most important monographs and catalogs which almost all contain extensive bibliographies, edited by Hella Robels

General
Peter Selz, *German Expressionist Painting,* University of California Press, Berkeley and Los Angeles, 1957

Brücke
Lothar-Günther Buchheim, *Die Künstlergemeinschaft Brücke,* Buchheim Verlag, Feldafing, 1956

Der Blaue Reiter
Lothar-Günther Buchheim, *Der Blaue Reiter und die "Neue Künstlervereinigung München,"* Buchheim Verlag, Feldafing, 1959

Dix
Fritz Löffler, *Otto Dix, Leben und Werk,* VEB Verlag der Kunst, Dresden, 1967²

Feininger
Hans Hess, *Lyonel Feininger,* W. Kohlhammer Verlag, Stuttgart, 1959. English edition published in London: Thames & Hudson, 1961 and New York: Harry N. Abrams, Inc., 1961
Lyonel Feininger — 1871—1956 — A Memorial Exhibition, Pasadena Art Museum, Milwaukee Art, Center, Baltimore Museum of Art, 1966

Grosz
J. J. H. Baur, *George Grosz,* New York, 1954
Herbert Bittner, *George Grosz,* Arts, Inc., New York — Verlag M. DuMont Schauberg, Köln, 1960, 1961

Heckel
Paul Vogt, *Erich Heckel,* Verlag Aurel Bongers, Recklinghausen, 1965

Jawlensky
Clemens Weiler, *Alexej Jawlensky,* Verlag M. DuMont Schauberg, Köln, 1959
Ewald Rathke, *Alexej Jawlensky,* Dr. Hans Peters Verlag, Hanau, 1968

Kandinsky
Will Grohmann, *Wassily Kandinsky, Leben und Werk,* Verlag M. DuMont Schauberg, Köln, 1958

Kirchner
Will Grohmann, *E. L. Kirchner,* W. Kohlhammer Verlag, Stuttgart, 1958
Exhibition catalogue: *Ernst Ludwig Kirchner,* Kunstverein für die Rheinlande und Westfalen, Düsseldorf, 1960
Donald E. Gordon, *Ernst Ludwig Kirchner,* Prestel-Verlag, München, 1968 and Harvard University Press, Cambridge (Mass.), 1968

Klee
Werner Haftmann, *Paul Klee — Wege Bildnerischen Denkens,* Prestel-Verlag, München, 1950
Carola Giedion-Welcker, *Paul Klee,* The Viking Press London, 1952
Will Grohmann, *Paul Klee,* W. Kohlhammer Verlag, Stuttgart, 1954
Will Grohmann, *Der Maler Paul Klee,* Verlag M. DuMont Schauberg, Köln, 1966

Kokoschka
Edith Hoffmann, *Kokoschka — Life and Work,* Faber & Faber Ltd., London, 1947
Hans Maria Wingler, *Oskar Kokoschka — Das Werk des Malers,* Verlag Galerie Welz, Salzburg, 1956

Kubin
Paul Raabe, *Alfred Kubin — Leben, Werk, Wirkung,* Rowohlt Verlag, Hamburg, 1957
Wieland Schmied, *Der Zeichner Alfred Kubin,* Residenz Verlag, Salzburg, 1967

Macke
Gustav Vriesen, *August Macke,* W. Kohlhammer Verlag, Stuttgart, 1957²

Moilliet
Exhibition catalogue: *Louis Moilliet,* Kunsthalle, Bern, 1963

Mueller
Lothar-Günther Buchheim, *Otto Mueller — Leben und Werk,* Buchheim Verlag, Feldafing, 1963

Nolde
Werner Haftmann, *Emil Nolde,* Verlag M. DuMont Schauberg, Köln, 1958

Pechstein

Max Osborn, *Max Pechstein,* Propyläen-Verlag, Berlin, 1922

Max Pechstein — Erinnerungen, edited by L. Reidemeister, Limes Verlag, Wiesbaden, 1960

Rohlfs

Paul Vogt, *Christian Rohlfs — Aquarelle und Zeichnungen,* Verlag Aurel Bongers, Recklinghausen, 1958

Walther Scheidig, *Christian Rohlfs,* VEB Verlag der Kunst, Dresden, 1965

Paul Vogt, *Chr. Rohlfs,* Verlag M. DuMont Schauberg, Köln, 1967

Schmidt-Rottluff

Will Grohmann, *Karl Schmidt-Rottluff,* Verlag W. Kohlhammer, Stuttgart, 1956

Gunther Thiem, *Karl Schmidt-Rottluff — Aquarelle und Zeichnungen,* Verlag F. Bruckmann, München, 1963

Feininger   HEILIGENHAFEN   Mont. d. 20. Feb. 1922

1962/60

Nolde.

Nolde.

Nolde.

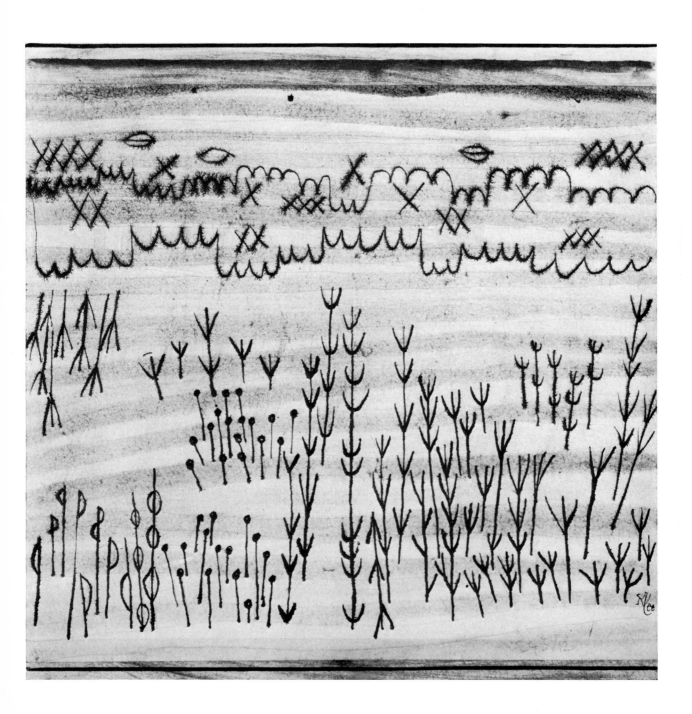

Since 1951, these watercolors were shown in the following exhibitions outside Germany:

Expressionisme. Werken uit de Verzameling Haubrich in het Wallraf-Richartz Museum te Keulen. Stedelijk Museum, Amsterdam, 1951.
L'expressionisme dans le Musée Wallraf-Richartz de Cologne. Palais des Beaux-Arts, Brussels, 1952.
Peintres expressionistes du Musée Wallraf-Richartz de Cologne. Collection Haubrich. Musée de L'Etat, Luxembourg, 1953.
Expressionisme e Arte Tedesca del 20° Secolo. Museo Civico, Torino, 1954.
Collections Wallraf-Richartz Museum de Cologne et Dr. Josef Haubrich. Musée des Beaux-Arts, Liège, 1955.
Moderne Sammlung des Wallraf-Richartz Museum, Köln, Sammlung Dr. Haubrich. Kunsthalle Basel, 1955.
Os Grandes Pintores do Expressionismo Alimáo Wallraf-Richartz Museum, Colonia: Colecao Haubrich. Museu de Arte Moderna, Sao Paulo, 1959.
Arte Alima desde 1945 Museu de Arte Moderna do Rio de Janeiro, 1960.
Aquarelles Dessins Rehaussés d'Expressionisme du Musée Wallraf-Richartz de Cologne, Goethe Institut, Paris; Maison de l'Europe, Menton; Goethe Institut, Marseille, 1965/66.